Can you name these animals?

We treat all animals, **big** and small!

Sam is the head vet. She has a team of people who all do different jobs.

Circle the people who work at the vet surgery.

| Surgeon | Nurse | Astronaut | Receptionist |

PARKING

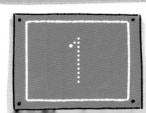  

FISH
live in water and breathe through flaps called gills.

MAMMALS
have fur or hair and feed their babies on milk.

AMPHIBIANS
live partly in water and partly on land.

How many animals are waiting?

Draw a line from each poster to one example of that kind of animal.

Woof woof!

In the waiting room

The first patients have arrived for their appointments. People keep all different kinds of pets.

BIRDS
have feathers and wings, and most can fly. All birds lay eggs.

REPTILES
live on land and have dry scaly skin. They lay eggs.

Good morning!

pets

Draw hands on the clock to show 8 o'clock.

Appointment time

Sam gives two kittens their first health check. She tells the owners how to care for their new pets.

The exam room has instruments and supplies in easy reach in case Sam needs them.

Find the equipment in the word search.

e	l	g	r	p	t	i	f	t	y	e
s	t	l	t	h	o	s	c	o	p	e
o	t	o	s	c	o	p	e	l	e	s
t	h	v	d	r	e	s	s	i	n	g
s	t	e	t	h	o	s	c	o	p	e
p	l	s	d	r	h	a	a	u	b	v
n	a	t	w	e	e	z	l	r	s	c
t	h	e	r	m	o	m	e	t	e	r
t	w	e	e	z	e	r	s	k	i	h

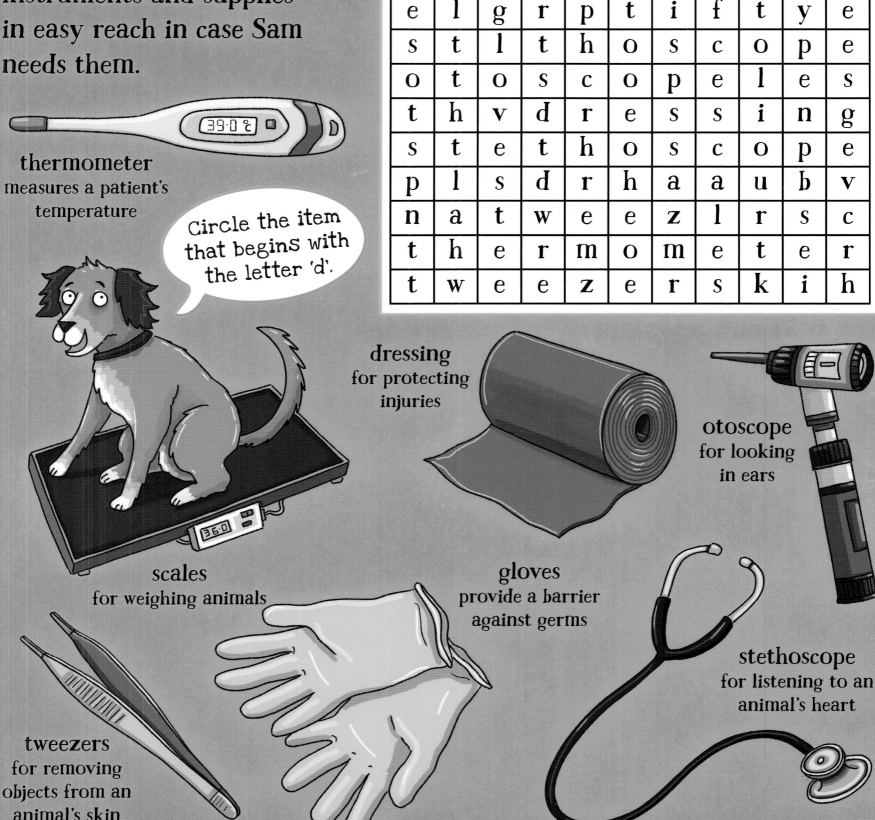

thermometer
measures a patient's temperature

Circle the item that begins with the letter 'd'.

scales
for weighing animals

tweezers
for removing objects from an animal's skin

dressing
for protecting injuries

gloves
provide a barrier against germs

otoscope
for looking in ears

stethoscope
for listening to an animal's heart

Rabbits and rodents

Next, Sam checks on the animals that have stayed overnight. Small mammals such as rabbits, mice and guinea pigs are looked after in their own area.

rabbit

Hay

Crisps

Grass

Water

Tea

Super scales

The reptile room needs to be kept warm, because reptiles are cold-blooded.

How many snakes can you see?

6

reptile

Many reptiles are brightly coloured. Circle the colour that's NOT in the picture.

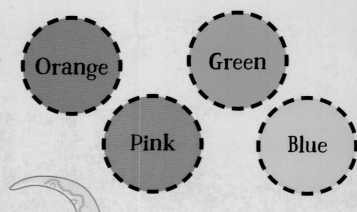

Orange

Green

Pink

Blue

Can you find the chameleon that's escaped from its cage?

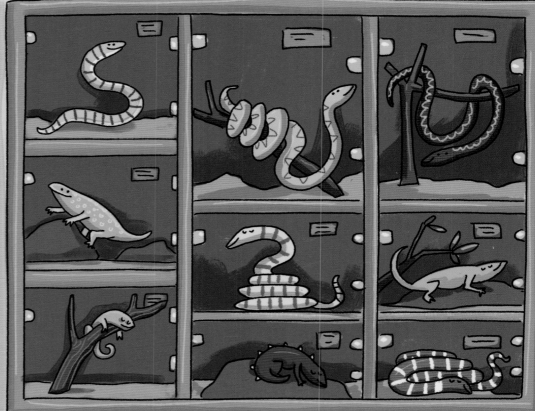

Another reptile is coming to stay. It has a hard shell. Circle the animal you think it is.

Iguana

Python

Tortoise

Lost and found

A lost dog has been brought in. Its collar is missing. A nurse scans the dog to see if it has a microchip they can use to get the owner's information. It does!

Trace the lines to find the microchip signal.

Find the way through the maze to take the dog back home.

A microchip is placed just under an animal's skin. Circle the position of the microchip on each animal.

Cat

Parrot

Horse

Taking X-rays

An X-ray is a special photograph that lets a vet see inside an animal's body. The vet surgery has an X-ray machine.

X-ray image

Circle and count the coins.

The X-ray shows that this dog has swallowed some coins!

X-ray machine

Animals often swallow things they shouldn't. Match these objects found in X-rays to the labels.

Paper clip   Button   Ring   Stick   Keys

Sam examines an X-ray of a cat that is limping. It shows that a bone in its leg is broken.

Circle the bone that is broken.

Colour in the X-ray.

cat

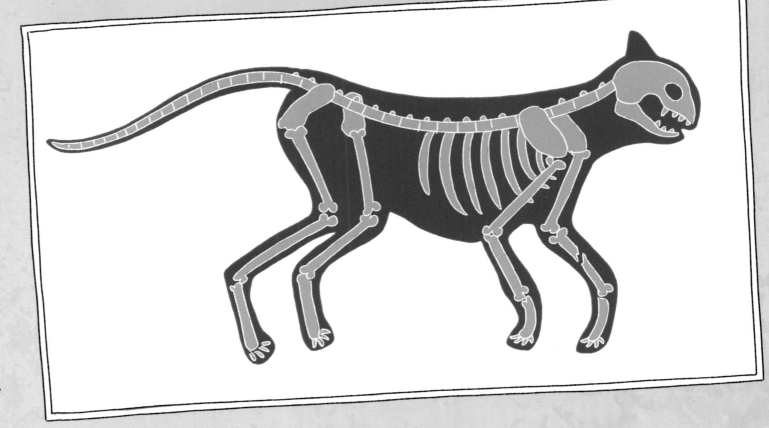

Can you link these X-rayed animals to their labels?

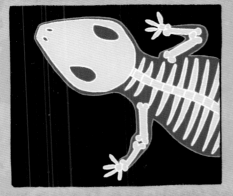 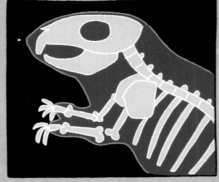 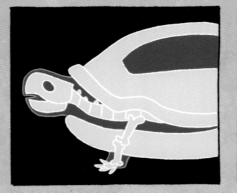 

Mouse   Tortoise   Goat   Lizard

Walking around cones in a figure-of-eight shape is good exercise.

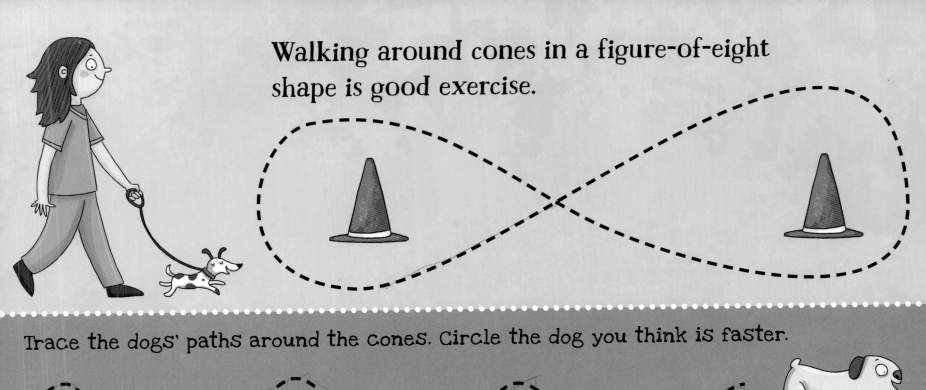

Trace the dogs' paths around the cones. Circle the dog you think is faster.

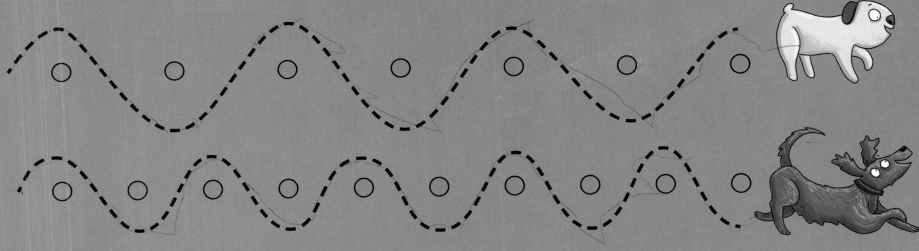

Circle two activities that improve a dog's balance.

ZOO

A zoo visit

Vets don't just treat pets. Some also look after zoo animals. This giraffe has just had a baby so the vet checks that both are healthy.

Vet's bag

Colour in my hooves and patches.

giraffe

This turtle was rescued from the sea because its shell was damaged. The vet makes sure it's completely healed.

Beak

Draw round the top plates on my shell.

The vet weighs all the penguin chicks to check they are a healthy weight.

How many chicks are waiting to be weighed?

6

Help the vet find the injured meerkat.

On the farm

One of the vets is visiting the local farm.

Ear

horse

Link the labels to the right parts of the horse.

Withers

Back

Tail

Nostril

Muzzle

Tick the boxes to give this horse her health check:

Not too thin or too fat ☐

Smooth, shiny coat ☐

Bright, clear eyes ☐

No broken teeth ☐

Knee

Hoof

Fetlock

Can you match these horses to their breed?

Shire horses are tall and strong with wispy fur around their hooves.

Shetland pony

Shire horse

Draw lines to link each horse to its name.

Animal babies

A man has brought in some ducklings that have lost their mother. Sam checks that they are healthy.

How many ducklings can you see?

10

Cheep cheep!

Vets need to know how to look after all kinds of animal babies.

Draw lines to match each animal to its baby.

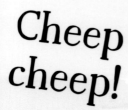

Owl

Calf

Piglet

Elephant

Pig

Owlet

Sometimes, vets make house calls to check on newborn animals. This cat has a healthy litter.

How many kittens are in the litter?

5

Puppies grow quickly. They have their first check-up at the vet at about 8 weeks old.

puppy

2 weeks old

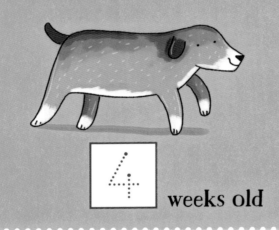

4 weeks old

8 weeks old

Baby rabbits need a check-up at five weeks old.

Catch the rabbits to take them to the vet.

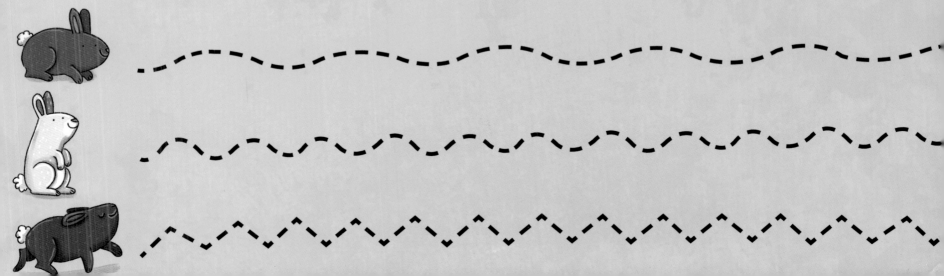

Good night!

It's a busy end to the day. The animals that need to stay overnight are settled in.

Draw hands on the clock to show 7 o'clock.

Kennel

1 2 3 4 5

People arrive to collect their pets.

Circle three things you can do at reception.

Pay the bill

Buy some milk

Make appointments

Get medicine

It's important to take a pet to and from the vet in the right type of carrier.

Match the animal to its carrier.

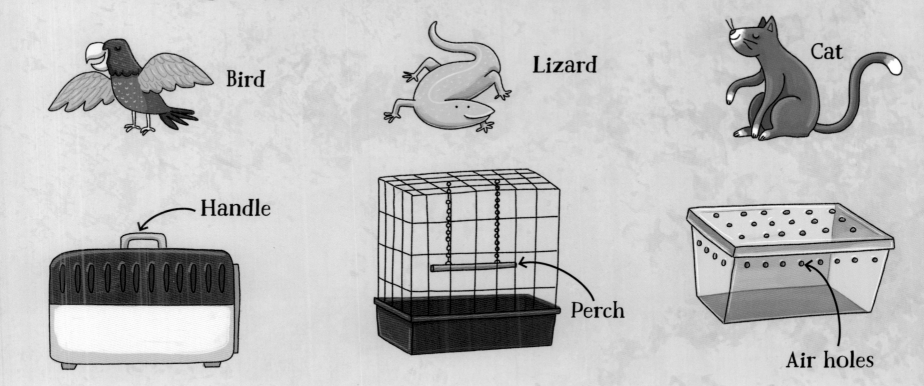

Bird

Lizard

Cat

Handle

Perch

Air holes

Some of the animals are taken to stay with foster families until they find homes.

Colour in the tyres.

Lots of space to keep animals safe inside

van

Miles Kelly

Hello! Welcome to the vet surgery.

Practise pen control and word and number skills while finding out about the work of a vet. Wipe the pages clean to complete the activities again and again.

Draw the hands on the clock

Complete the word search

Count the animals

Learn about lots of animals too!

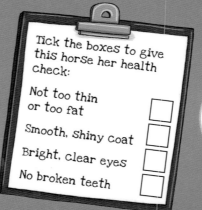

Tick the boxes to give this horse her health check:

Not too thin or too fat ☐

Smooth, shiny coat ☐

Bright, clear eyes ☐

No broken teeth ☐

How many bees can you spot inside this book?

Is your pen wipe-clean? Test it here

Illustrated by Richard Watson
Written by Amy Johnson
Designed by Jo Cowan
Copyright © 2019 Miles Kelly Publishing Ltd
Harding's Barn, Bardfield End Green,
Thaxted, Essex, CM6 3PX, UK
All rights reserved

UK £5.99
US $7.95

ISBN 978-1-78617-779-7
Printed in China, Mar 2019, LGV19
9 781786 177797

www.Miles Kelly.net

TITLES IN THIS SERIES:
Castle · Farm
Fire Station · Vet

KU-840-714